Make America Grape Again
ISBN-13: 9780692096796
Written by Jeff Durston
Illustrated by Hannah Howerton
Copyright © 2018 Jeff Durston
Printed in PRC
www.makeamericagrapeagainbook.com
Follow @grapeagainbook

FOR MY KIDS

MAKE AMERICA GRAPE AGAIN

WRITTEN BY JEFF DURSTON & ILLUSTRATED BY HANNAH HOWERTON

HOW ONE MISGUIDED ORANGE
ALMOST RUINED
THE WHOLE FRUIT SALAD

There once was a country so nice and so sweet
A place full of fruit, but not the kind that you eat

They all lived together in the juiciest of lands
There were apples with legs, there were lemons with hands

There were prickly pineapples and melons with seeds
There were overripe pears and fuzzy kiwis

There were round watermelons the size of your head
You'd see grapes of all colors: green, purple, and red

The papayas had eyes, the peaches had teeth
They'd smile at each other as they passed on the street

The older bananas would show off their brown
To the younger and greener bananas in town

The peaches and prunes would play at the park
With mangoes all day until well after dark

The fruit, they would tell you, the key to their glee
Was their differences, it was their diversity

I wish I could tell you this country of fruit
Never had a bad day, never lost the pursuit
Of its values and morals, its lofty ideals
But not all the fruit beneath their bright peels
Were happy and sweet, some juice had gone sour

And soon at a strange and remarkable hour
An outspoken orange appeared on TV
He smirked and he said to the fruit family

"Not everyone here in this country of fruit
Can stay as they please, so let's give 'em the boot!
We'll find all the fruit that looks different or weird
And we'll send them away!" He said with a sneer.

"We'll start with the overly green cantaloupes
And you misshapen pears, we've got you on the ropes!"

"The hairy kiwis, the strange looking melons
Those imported mangoes are probably felons!"

"I'm tired of looking at imperfect food
Whose peels aren't as bright or as perfectly smooth
As my bright orange skin – can't you see that I'm great?
I have fabulous color and texture and weight."

"Not like those raisins with their wrinkly skin
Let's Make America Grape Again!"

As you might imagine this caused quite a fright
And some of the fruit started saying, "He's right."

They marched in the streets and believed in this story
That the orange was there to restore all their glory
The only way forward, they came to believe
Was to tell all the imperfect fruit they should leave

But luckily some of the fruit had the mind
Not to listen to him and his fans, the Alt-Rind

They knew that what mattered the most in the end
Was that all of the fruit, they could learn to be friends

So they gathered together and made their own chants
They planned their own marches, they sang and they danced

They gathered donations and made protest signs
They put down their phones and picked up The Times
And after a while, not an hour or three
Not a day or a month but eventually

All of the fruit, well they came to their senses
And realized their lives were not better with fences

They took off their stickers to show that they thought
Whether bumpy or smooth, organic or not
Whether packed full of seeds or a core or a pit
Their differences they didn't matter one bit

And the finest fruit salad could still lose its way
If it split up to look like a Lunchables tray

They learned that respect shows a nation's true wealth
And who taught them this lesson? Well, that orange himself

Because sometimes it takes something nasty and sour
To show us what's sweet and remind us our power
Comes not from our I's or our me's but to trust
That we'll all be okay if we just stick with us